Gardens

Charming pull-out line drawings
to bring to life with colour

This edition published by Parragon Books Ltd in 2015

Parragon Books Ltd
Chartist House
15–17 Trim Street
Bath BA1 1HA, UK
www.parragon.com

Copyright © Parragon Books Ltd 2014-2015
Illustrated by David Thelwell and James McGairy

ISBN 978-1-4723-8219-1

Printed in China

Bath · New York · Cologne · Melbourne · Delhi
Hong Kong · Shenzhen · Singapore · Amsterdam